Over recent years Chronic Fatigue Syndrome in its various manifestations has become a major source of impairment and distress to many children and families. Whilst there remains controversy about the nature of the condition, it is increasingly recognised that the outcome is better in children than in adults, the majority recovering even if some retain a tendency to tire easily. It is also increasingly clear that adequate management can substantially help towards improvement and recovery. Trudie Chalder has pioneered the development of treatment programmes for young people. The programmes usually involve adopting a consistent approach to activities, a gradual increase in activities, establishing a sleep routine and other CBT techniques. Her work is helping to establish a scientific basis for treatment approaches in this field. As reflected in this excellently written and presented book, it will guide and inspire not only young people affected by CFS but also clinicians helping them towards rehabilitation.

The book describes the principles underlying the authors' clinical work. It provides young people with a homework manual to use as active participants in their own recovery, whilst enabling them to become more autonomous and competent. It comes highly recommended and may be predicted to become a basic tool in the management of young people with CFS.

Professor Elena GARRALDA, MD, Mphil, FRCPsych, FRCPCH
Faculty of Medicine, Imperial College of Science,
Technology and Medicine

June 2002

Acknowledgements

We would like to thank the children and parents who have given us feedback on this guide. Vincent Deary and Simon Darnley also gave feedback on the content. We would like to acknowledge:

Gillian Butler and Tony Hope's Manage Your Mind: the Mental Fitness Guide (1995; BCA Oxford University Press).

David D. Burns' Feeling Good, The New Mood Therapy (1980; Avon Books, New York)

Mary Burgess & Trudie Chalder: Chronic Fatigue Syndrome Self-Help Treatment Manual.

Pauline Powell: Chronic Fatigue Syndrome. What you need to get better.

Finally we thank South Thames Research and Development Project Grant Scheme for funding our research.

CONTENTS

C.F.S.

WHAT IS CFS?

Everybody feels tired sometimes, but if you feel tired a lot of the time, you might have a condition called **Chronic Fatigue Syndrome (CFS)**. Some people call it **M.E.** or **Post Viral Fatigue Syndrome.**

CFS is the name given to a condition where you feel very tired most of the time, and have done so for at least 6 months. Along with physical tiredness you have 'mental' tiredness, which may lead you to have problems concentrating, problems with your memory, or with finding the right word. You may have other symptoms along with the fatigue, for example, muscle pain, headaches and sleep problems. Resting may not relieve the tiredness.

For a doctor to decide that you have CFS, he or she will first carry out routine investigations to find the cause of your fatigue. If no medical problem has been found, which may be making you feel like this, and you have been checked by a paediatrician, your condition can be described as CFS.

As you can see, the name *describes* your condition. 'Chronic' means long-term, 'fatigue' is another word for tiredness, and a 'syndrome' is a particular group of symptoms that go together to form part of an illness. The name is neutral in that it doesn't imply that there is a cause for your illness. This is deliberate, as a specific cause for CFS has not been found.

Feeling tired is quite common in young people, but CFS, the illness, is rare for young people. A recent survey found that 1 in 500 young people had felt tired for a long time, but only 1 in 2,500 had CFS.

CFS is a controversial condition. Some people do not believe that it is a real illness. However a report published by the Department of Health in January 2002 has stated that doctors should recognise CFS as a long term illness that can severely affect people of all ages.

Different doctors often give different advice on how to recover from CFS. You may have already received differing advice as to how to get better. This can be upsetting and confusing, on top of already feeling unwell.

We know that people with CFS really are ill but we believe that they can be helped.

WHY DID YOU GET IT?

Nobody really knows why people get CFS. It can start after an illness like flu or glandular fever, or after a stressful time in your life such as working very hard for exams, or after a big change in your life, like going to a new school. It is likely that the causes of your CFS will differ to the reasons which keep the illness going, once it has been triggered. These will be slightly different for each sufferer.

Some of the things which contribute to keeping your CFS going can be changed! **This guide will help you to work on these things.**

WHAT KEEPS CFS GOING?

A number of things are likely to have contributed to the onset of your CFS but it's likely that once triggered, different factors keep the fatigue and disability going. **Listed below are some of the reasons.**

Your body is unfit

If you've been ill for a while, and have cut down on your activities, your body will not be used to doing very much and it will be unfit in a number of ways. Your muscles will be weaker and producing less energy because they haven't been used as much, leaving you with less stamina. If you suddenly try to do more your muscles will hurt. This is not because of muscle disease **but because they are out of condition.**

One of the jobs of the muscles is to squeeze blood back to the heart from the body. If your muscles are weak and small, they cannot do this very well, so blood collects in the legs and less goes to the brain, making you feel dizzy. The circulation of blood around the body is reduced, the amount of oxygen your blood carries is reduced, your blood pressure becomes lower and your heart rate gets higher. These things can lead to many different symptoms: dizziness when you stand up, feeling hot and cold, sweating, feeling unsteady and clumsy, breathless, fatigued, nauseous, feeling dull mentally and being less able to do exercise.

Remember, if you don't use it you lose it!

See-sawing

You may be see-sawing between doing a lot on a day when you feel good and resting on a day when you feel tired or unwell. It's important to keep a balance between rest and activity everyday, and to stick to a similar routine everyday. **Not sticking to a regular routine can upset the timings of your 'body clock' which controls rhythms in your body.** This can make you feel generally unwell, with symptoms such as headaches, poor concentration and alertness, low energy and poor quality sleep.

Being afraid of making things worse

You and your parents may understandably feel afraid of making the CFS worse. You may have been given different advice from different doctors about how to cope with CFS and it wouldn't be surprising if you feel confused about whether activity may harm your body or make you worse. Perhaps when you have tried to go back to your normal activities the CFS has got worse. It seems sensible to rest when you're tired, but this only helps for a little while. Rest does not help illnesses that have lasted a long time. **In fact the more you rest the more fatigued you will feel.**

9

Being too tough on yourself

You may have played a lot of sports before or been used to doing lots of activities. You might be expecting yourself to get better and return to that level of activity very quickly. During a period of rest, fit and active people lose a lot more fitness than unfit people. They therefore need longer than unfit people to return to their previous fitness level. Maybe you are pushing yourself too hard and expect changes too quickly. During your recovery period don't expect yourself to perform at your previous level. **It will take time and practice to return to get back to normal.**

Don't be too hard on yourself! Research has shown that young people with CFS and their parents underestimate how much activity they have actually done! They also underestimated how tired healthy adolescents actually get. Do what you can manage and don't give yourself a hard time.

Symptom focusing

When you've had a symptom for a long time it's understandable that you will be worried about it. The more you worry about it, the more you'll notice it. **The more you notice it and respond to it, the bigger the problem will become!**

Feeling frustrated and/or low.

You may feel low at times and that is to be expected as CFS is a distressing illness. You may feel that you can't do anything about your CFS, that you don't know why it's happening or how long it will last. All these worries are understandable and will add to you feeling worse.

Worries

Not doing things regularly makes you lose confidence in yourself. You may be worried, for example, about going back to school and what you've missed, or that your friends are moving on without you. This can mean Double Trouble – you have to cope with these worries and the CFS. **Again these worries will add to you feeling worse.**

We can summarise how CFS may start and what can keep it going in the diagram overleaf. All of the things described above may not apply to you, but perhaps you can see some of these things at work in your own illness. **The diagram shows how each thing affects the others and how it is easy to get caught up in a vicious circle of worsening fatigue and symptoms.**

ILLNESS and/or STRESS FATIGUE

REST & REDUCED ACTIVI

FRUSTRATION & WORRY
About not being able to
carry out normal activities

BODY BECOMES UNFIT,
DISTURBED BODY CLOCK
Symptoms and difficulty
with taking up activity

LOSS OF CONFIDENCE
inability to go back to normal activities

REST & REDUCED ACTIVI

REST & REDUCED ACTIVITY

BODY BECOMES MORE UNFIT,
MORE DISTURBED BODY CLOCK
Further symptoms and more
difficulty on taking up activity

FEAR OF CFS GETTING WORSE

SYMPTOM FOCUSING
Worry about, and focus on,
worsening symptoms

Summary

Stress or an infection can leave you feeling tired. It is normal to rest in response to tiredness or to cut down on activities. However if you rest too much, or your body loses its fitness, you will feel more tired than usual when you return to your usual activities and you may have symptoms such as dizziness.

If resting has meant that your sleep pattern has changed, your 'body clock' may have been disrupted. Because of the effects on your body you will find it harder to perform normal activities.

If you've experienced unpleasant symptoms on returning to normal activities, you may have lost your confidence. You may worry that you will never be able to do the things you used to. The frustration and worry also contributes to feeling tired and lacking in energy.

Now that we have explained how we think your CFS may have got started, and then carried on, we can show you how to tackle the factors that may be keeping it going.

HELP IS ON THE WAY...!

AIM OF THIS GUIDE

This guide is written for young people from the ages of about 10 years to about 18 years, but could be useful also for people a little younger or older than this. The guide is based on a self-help programme for CFS with young people. We evaluated this programme and found that after a certain type of treatment, called cognitive behaviour therapy (CBT), the majority of the young people who participated were less tired and were attending school at least 75% of the time. After 6 months, all the young people who had completed the CBT programme were back at school and 95% of them were attending full-time. As well as feeling less tired, most of them reported improvements in their social lives and had fewer worries.

What is CBT?

Cognitive Behavioural Therapy (or CBT for short) is a therapeutic treatment that has been shown to be helpful for CFS. The word *'cognitive'* means *'how you think'* and *'behavioural'* means *'how you behave or act'*. All this means is that this form of therapy will help you to do things differently and perhaps think a little differently – this will make you feel differently as well. We've found that CBT helps people with CFS and is completely safe. It is used successfully for other illnesses, as well, such as diabetes or chronic pain.

Although CBT is not a 'cure' for CFS, the research described above showed that it can reduce the symptoms of CFS and can help people return to their normal activities, so improving their well-being and quality of life. These improvements seem to be long-term.

This guide is based on a CBT approach and will give you ideas about how you might try and tackle your CFS. **However, be patient – CBT is not an overnight cure.** It takes time and you will have to work at it with the help of your family. Your mum, dad, brothers and sisters can also benefit by learning and practising a little CBT themselves while helping you along the way.

When to see a therapist?

You can use this book as a guide if you want to try to help yourself to overcome your CFS. However, sometimes, if your CFS is very severe or if you find it difficult to understand the ideas in this guide or you are having difficulty motivating yourself enough to stick to the things that have been suggested, **you may find it helpful to also see a therapist. Your General Practitioner should be able to help you to get in touch with a therapist who can help you. It would probably be helpful if the therapist was trained in Cognitive Behavioural Therapy (CBT).** Your therapist and you could also work together through some of the steps introduced in this guide.

Some Words of Caution

If you are feeling extremely low in mood and very depressed, or are even at times thinking of ending your life or suffer from other emotional problems that are too severe for you to be able to benefit from a self-help guide alone, it is important that you tell your GP so that the right type of professional help can be arranged for you. Don't be shy of asking – the sooner you get help the sooner there is a chance for you to feel better.

WAYS
TO HELP YOU GET BETTER

SLEEP MANAGEMENT

People with CFS often have problems sleeping. You may find it hard to go to sleep, or wake up during the night, or need a lot of sleep. When you wake up you may feel exhausted and still feel sleepy during the day. Your sleep pattern may vary wildly from day to day.

The 'Body Clock'

Our sleep is controlled by a 'body clock' which also controls other rhythms in your body, like appetite, body temperature and alertness. The clock needs to be 'reset' each day by signals to your body such as waking and going to bed times, mealtimes, activity and exercise.

What happens if it slips?

If your body does not receive these signals the timing of its rhythms start to slip. This can make you feel tired, unwell, and low, make it hard to concentrate, and give you headaches, muscle pain, make you lose your appetite and give you poor sleep.

Why does it slip?

Your body clock can easily be disrupted by staying up too late and sleeping in, sleeping during the day, or not being active enough during the day. Perhaps your body clock has been disrupted by you taking more rest in response to an infection or feeling unwell, or being kept awake at night by stress.

Not having a regular routine such as going to bed and getting up at different times each day, or taking catnaps during the day, or even sleeping too much can disturb your body clock.

How NOT to cope!

Although it may seem like the sensible thing to do and make you feel better in the short term, coping with disrupted sleep or with feeling tired by **sleeping during the day does not help!** It will reduce the quality of your night-time sleep and confuses your body clock further.

However you can reset your body clock! Here's how...

How to reset your body clock and make your sleep better

🕐 **Make a 'Bedtime-Uptime' routine**

Get up at the same time everyday. Use an alarm clock – put it on the other side of the room so that you have to get up to switch it off. This will help you avoid constantly pressing the snooze button! Draw back your curtains to let in the light. Get up at the same time no matter what time you went to bed. If your sleep is very disrupted you may have to do this gradually by setting yourself a slightly earlier time to get up each week. The next section explains how to do this. You should aim to be sleeping for about 8 hours only. Sleeping more than this makes you feel slowed down and makes you feel you need even more sleep.

🕐 **Don't sleep during the day**

If this is a habit of yours you might want to cut down your daytime sleep gradually by reducing it every week. The next section explains how to do this.

🕐 **Use your bed only for sleeping**

Don't watch TV or read in bed. Try not to use it during the day. Your bed will then become a signal only for sleep. If you've been in bed for more than 20 minutes and haven't fallen asleep, go to another room and do something relaxing until you do feel sleepy again. Do this as many times as you have to. It will help to make your bed a signal for sleeping only. Do the same thing if you wake up in the night and can't get back to sleep.

Achieving good quality sleep

You may find keeping a diary of your sleep patterns helpful. *(See Chart A)* **Use this to record your sleep habits for a week.** Work out how long you spend actually asleep at night on average. For example you may spend 10 hours in bed each night but only sleep for 6 hours. To make your sleep efficient, so you don't spend time in bed lying awake, only spend the average number of hours in bed that you are actually asleep. So if you sleep on average for 6 hours a night, only spend 6 hours in bed, whether you have slept for 6 hours or not. You may feel you haven't slept enough or feel tired the next morning but if you stick to it, this method will make your sleep deeper, less broken, and you will fall asleep faster. Once you have achieved this sleep of better quality you can increase the time you spend asleep to up to 8 eight hours.

Getting ready for bed

An hour before bed try to wind down and relax – don't study or exercise but watch TV or have a warm bath or read. **Do things in the same order before going to bed.** These will become signals to your body that you're getting ready for sleep.

Can't sleep?

If you go to bed and find you can't fall asleep try these tricks:

- Don't start worrying about not being able to fall asleep. Reassure yourself that "sleep will come when it's ready" and "relaxing in bed is almost as good".

- Keep your eyes open in the dark and try to keep them open as sleep tries to close them.

- Imagine a pleasant scene where you are feeling relaxed and peaceful.

- Relax the different areas of your body one by one, and breathe slowly and deeply

- If you haven't fallen asleep in 20 minutes or find that you're not sleepy anymore get up and go to another room until you feel sleepy again.

Have a Worry Time

If you can't sleep because you keep worrying then make yourself a **'Worry Time'**. This can be a slot during the day when you can think and talk about any worries you have and what you can do to help them. Sometimes it helps to write them down. You may want to use the **Problem Solving Method** described later. **If you find yourself worrying in bed tell yourself you'll deal with the problem during Worry Time.**

You may wonder why you have to stick to these rules about going to sleep while other people do not need to. But if you are suffering from unpleasant symptoms because of a disturbed sleep routine this is the only way to relieve them.

Changing your habits will be difficult but sticking with these rules will mean that in a few weeks you will not have to suffer from the symptoms caused by a disrupted body clock. You may feel worse to begin with and find that you are not sleeping very much. Don't sleep in the day to make up for it. After a few weeks of sticking to these rules you will begin to feel better and your sleep will improve. As you incorporate more activity and exercise into your routine you will find that the quality of your sleep improves further.

ACTIVITY SCHEDULING

People usually think that if they're tired they need more rest. On the whole the opposite is true - they may actually need more activity or exercise!

If you always rest when you feel unwell the CFS will start to control you. CBT will help you control the CFS! If you have coped with CFS by resting a lot or cutting down on your activities, or only getting on with things when you feel well enough, it is more than likely that your body has lost its fitness.

You probably have a number of things you would like to be able to do again. **The aim of this part of CBT is to slowly help your body achieve fitness and greater stamina** so that you can build up your activities and achieve these goals.

1. What are you doing at the moment?

Keep a diary of your activity for a couple of weeks *(See Chart B).* For each hour jot down what you are doing, even if it is sitting 'doing nothing'. Keeping the diary will accurately show you how you are spending your time, and make it easier to see what sort of changes you want to make. The diary may show that you are getting up at very different times each day, or perhaps living in a 'boom and bust' way where you collapse with exhaustion at the end of the day, or at the weekend.

2. What Changes do you want to make?

Take a while to think about how you would like to change your current activity. You might want to change your sleeping pattern, or be able to take a short walk, or be able to study. Once you have achieved these goals, you may want to introduce new activities into your time, like playing a favourite sport or playing an instrument, or other hobby, or perhaps seeing more of your friends. Write down the goals you would like to achieve. *Keep them realistic and achievable. Be specific about exactly what you would like to do, how often you'd like to do it and for how long,* if appropriate.

Below are some examples of goals that young people set themselves.

- 🕐 To get up at 9.30 am
- 🕐 To walk 10 minutes twice a day, once in the morning and once in the afternoon
- 🕐 To study for 30 minutes in the morning and 30 minutes in the afternoon.

Obviously the goals and targets you set for yourself will depend on how badly the CFS affects you and the type of activities that you would like to be able to do but cannot. They will be different for different people.

Whatever your goals, remember to keep them realistic so that you can achieve them consistently. As you improve you can make your goals slightly more challenging, but still within reach.

3. How can you make those changes?

Next, you will have to work out how you can get to your goals. Write down small steps or targets which will build towards achieving your goal. **Use the Goal Breakdown sheet** *(Chart C)*. The targets should be tiny chunks of activity that you can practice often, if appropriate. Make the first target something you can easily do and make the next targets slightly harder each time.

For example:

Goal:
To get up at 9.30am.

Targets:
To get up at 10.30am each day
To get up at 10.00am each day
To get up at 9.30am each day

Goal:
To walk 10 minutes twice a day, once in the morning and once in the afternoon.

Targets:
To walk 2 minutes twice a day
To walk 5 minutes twice a day
To walk 7 minutes twice a day
To walk 10 minutes twice a day

Goal:
To study for 30 minutes in the morning and 30 minutes in the afternoon.

Targets:
To study for 5 minutes in the morning and afternoon
To study for 10 minutes in the morning and afternoon
To study for 15 minutes in the morning and afternoon
To study for 20 minutes in the morning and afternoon
To study for 30 minutes in the morning and afternoon

4. Make your life balanced

The first step in changing your activity habits is to achieve a balanced day. **Look at your current activity on your Activity Diaries.** Then plan your next couple of weeks so that you are doing *the same amount of activity and having the same amount of rest, divided into small easy chunks, spread evenly throughout the day and week. Use the Activity Schedule form (Chart D) to write out your plan for the week.* When resting try not to sleep or lie down, and rest in the sitting room rather than your bedroom.

Do your best to stick to the plan whether you feel up to it or not. It's important that you don't do more than you planned if you feel good, but equally important to stick to your routine even when you feel unwell.

After a couple of weeks, once you are in the habit of living in a more balanced way you can add new activities to your routine.

5. Add a target

Choose one or more target from your **Goal Breakdown** sheet that you know you can and will carry out. Whatever you choose, do it little and often.

You can keep track of how well you are doing on the **Pathways Toward Change form** *(Chart E).* In the left hand column write down your activity targets for a particular week, and in the right hand columns, rate how far you stuck to your target for each day, if appropriate. If you find that you are not sticking to your targets, this means you should lower them until you can achieve them, and then gradually build up to harder levels. This form will help you keep track of the progress you are making.

6. Add more targets

Carry on with your plan of activity until you can do it without any trouble. This should take a week or two. You will be able to see whether you are completing your targets successfully on the **Pathways Towards Change form** *(Chart E)*. Then replace the first target you set yourself in your Weekly Plan with the next target from your Goal Breakdown sheet. Note how well you can carry out the plan, and once you can do it without difficulty, you can take set yourself the next target.

Gradually you will work your way up your targets and build up your exercise and activities. **Over time, the amount of rest you take should decrease and the amount of time you spend on activities should increase.**

Rules for adding activities to your routine

- Do very small chunks of this activity spread throughout the day and week.

- Start at a level that you can do easily. This will mean you won't have a relapse of symptoms and fatigue when you begin to change your habits.

- Don't do more than you planned or less. Even if you are having a bad day stick to your plan and do at least as much as you did the day before. This will stop your body from losing the fitness that it has gained.

- Don't worry if you notice your symptoms increase when you start to follow the program. You may feel dizzy, breathless, and tired. It's usual to feel tired at first but this will go. It doesn't mean that that the CBT isn't working, or that the CFS is getting worse. Your body is just getting used to it.

- Don't give up! You may feel disheartened if the progress you are making is slow. But if you stick with it and make slow but steady progress you will gradually improve. Keep your old activity diaries and schedules to remind yourself how far you have come. The time it takes to recover your fitness is much longer than it takes to lose the fitness you have. **So be patient and persevere.**

Eventually you'll reach your long-term goals!

For those who those who are severely affected

CFS affects people to varying extents. Some sufferers are bed bound, restricted to a wheelchair and not able to do very much activity. If CFS affects you this severely, the activities that you begin with may be sitting up or getting out of bed for a few minutes, building up to standing for a few minutes or climbing a few stairs.

For those who are less affected by CFS

You may be attending school full-time but find yourself exhausted at the end of the day and have no energy at the weekends. Or there may be some aspects of your life which you don't have the energy for anymore, like playing a sport or keeping up a hobby. You may be living in a boom and bust way, where on good days you achieve a lot and on bad days you only rest. If this describes you, you can also use the **Activity Scheduling** described above to balance your day and week with consistent rest and activity, and gradually build in aspects of your life that you have neglected

CHANGING UNHELPFUL THOUGHTS

Having CFS can make you feel low. It can be hard to believe things will get better.

- *Have you noticed that when you feel low, you sometimes have horrible, negative or unhelpful thoughts?*
- *Have you noticed that when you feel happy you think positive confident things?*
- *When we're feeling down it can help us to think about things from different angles, even if we don't necessarily have confidence in these viewpoints.*

Sad thoughts can be automatic because they pop up by themselves and can be difficult to get rid of. They can seem sensible but they might not be quite true.

You could keep a diary of these sad or unhelpful thoughts *(See Chart F).* You'll have to practice 'catching' them. Keep an eye on your mood. If it gets low **think back to what you were thinking just before your mood got worse.**

When you have an unhelpful or sad thought try to think of an alternative more helpful, positive view of things instead. It can help to ask yourself the questions on the next page. They will help you to see whether what you're thinking is completely true.

It is important not to confuse a thought with a fact. Just because you think or feel something to be true, it doesn't mean that it is.

You'll realise that there are many different ways of looking at things. You may find it helpful to keep a diary of helpful alternative thoughts that you think of (Chart F).

29

When you have a ask yourself these questions.

They will help you to think of more

Q.: Am I thinking in Black and White?

I DIDN'T GET AN 'A' FOR THIS ESSAY. IT'S COMPLETELY RUBBISH!

HANG ON! I DID GET A 'B'. IT MIGHT NOT BE THE TOP MARK BUT IT MUST MEAN I WROTE A DECENT ESSAY AND I'VE LEARNT ABOUT THE TOPIC.

Q.: Am I forgetting the good things?

THERE'S SO MUCH TO DO. I'M NOT GETTING ANYWHERE. IT'S NOT WORKING!

BUT WHAT ABOUT ALL THE THINGS I HAVE DONE? I MUSTN'T FORGET THEM. THEY STILL COUNT. I HAVE MADE SOME PROGRESS.

Q.: Am I predicting the future?

I'LL NEVER GET BETTER!

I HAVEN'T GOT A CRYSTAL BALL. There's no reason why I shouldn't

Q.: Am I reading other people's minds?

EVERYONE IS FED UP WITH ME.

HOW DO I KNOW THAT? THEY HAVEN'T SAID THEY ARE FED UP WITH ME. THEY MAY JUST BE TOO BUSY TO TALK TO ME AT THE MOMENT. THEY MAY HAVE OTHER THINGS ON THEIR MIND, OR MAYBE THEY ARE FEELING FED UP FOR SOME OTHER REASON.

Q.: Am I being too hard on myself (or others)?

> I'M NOT GOOD ENOUGH. I SHOULD BE DOING BETTER THAN THIS.

> WHO SAYS I SHOULD BE DOING BETTER? I'M DOING THE BEST THAT I CAN CONSIDERING HOW ILL I AM, AND THAT'S ALL I CAN DO.

Q.: Am I thinking the worst?

> I FEEL SO ILL. I KNOW I'LL HAVE A RELAPSE AND BE WORSE THAN BEFORE

> I'M THINKING OF THE WORST POSSIBLE OUTCOME! IT DOESN'T HAVE TO END IN DISASTER! I MAY NOT GET WORSE. IF I DO IT MIGHT NOT BE THAT BAD, OR I MIGHT EVEN FEEL BETTER.

Q.: Am I labelling myself, (or others)?

> I CAN'T HELP MUM WITH THE HOUSEWORK BECAUSE I'M SO TIRED. I'M JUST USELESS!

> I MIGHT NOT BE ABLE TO HELP MUM RIGHT NOW, BUT THAT DOESN'T MEAN THAT I ALWAYS HAVE BEEN AND ALWAYS WILL BE 'USELESS' IN EVERY SITUATION. IN FACT THERE ARE WAYS THAT I CAN BE HELPFUL, EVEN IF I CAN'T DO VERY MUCH PHYSICALLY. I CAN HELP MUM WHEN SHE NEEDS SOMEONE TO DISCUSS IDEAS WITH. NOT EVERYONE IS PERFECT ALL THE TIME.

Q.: Am I taking things personally?

> WHY IS IT ALWAYS ME THAT HAS ALL THESE PROBLEMS?

> I DO HAVE PROBLEMS RIGHT NOW BUT THERE HAVE BEEN TIMES WHEN THINGS HAVE GONE WELL FOR ME. THINKING ABOUT IT, MY FRIENDS HAVE ALSO HAD PROBLEMS THEY HAVE HAD TO DEAL WITH BEFORE. IT'S NOT JUST ME WHO IS HAVING TO DEAL WITH PROBLEMS.

Q.: Am I thinking something is true just because it feels that way?

I FEEL SO HOPELESS. IT'S ALL A WASTE OF TIME.

OK, SO I FEEL HOPELESS AND I THINK IT'S A WASTE OF TIME. IT DOESN'T MEAN THAT THINGS *REALLY ARE* HOPELESS AND IT *REALLY IS* A WASTE OF TIME. IT'S JUST THE WAY I'M FEELING AT THE MOMENT.

You might have negative thoughts to do with certain worries, like school and exams, or the CFS getting worse, or problems with family or friends. **Again, ask yourself the questions above, to help you look at things in a more helpful way.**

For example you may have the following unhelpful thoughts to do with...

SCHOOL AND EXAMS...

The thought of catching up on all the work you've missed can be daunting.

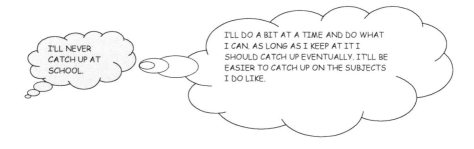

I'LL NEVER CATCH UP AT SCHOOL.

I'LL DO A BIT AT A TIME AND DO WHAT I CAN. AS LONG AS I KEEP AT IT I SHOULD CATCH UP EVENTUALLY. IT'LL BE EASIER TO CATCH UP ON THE SUBJECTS I DO LIKE.

Waiting for exam results can be nerve-wracking.

I'VE MISSED SO MUCH - I'VE PROBABLY DONE RUBBISH.

THERE'S QUITE A BIT OF WORK I DID COVER. THE RESULTS I'VE HAD SO FAR HAVE BEEN PASSES. I'VE DONE BETTER THAN SOME OTHER PEOPLE WHO HAVEN'T MISSED ANY TIME FROM SCHOOL. I'LL SEE WHAT I GET INSTEAD OF GETTING MYSELF DOWN BEFORE I'VE EVEN GOT MY RESULTS.

WHAT IF MY RESULTS ARE REALLY BAD?

AS LONG AS I TRIED MY BEST AT THE TIME, THAT'S WHAT COUNTS.

CFS...

The thought of the CFS coming back or getting worse can be scary.

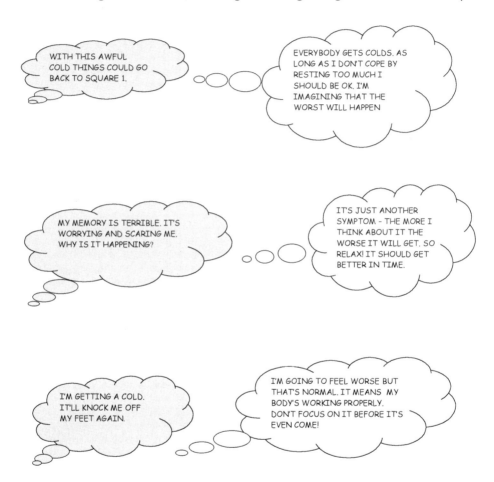

WITH THIS AWFUL COLD THINGS COULD GO BACK TO SQUARE 1.

EVERYBODY GETS COLDS. AS LONG AS I DON'T COPE BY RESTING TOO MUCH I SHOULD BE OK. I'M IMAGINING THAT THE WORST WILL HAPPEN

MY MEMORY IS TERRIBLE. IT'S WORRYING AND SCARING ME. WHY IS IT HAPPENING?

IT'S JUST ANOTHER SYMPTOM - THE MORE I THINK ABOUT IT THE WORSE IT WILL GET. SO RELAX! IT SHOULD GET BETTER IN TIME.

I'M GETTING A COLD. IT'LL KNOCK ME OFF MY FEET AGAIN.

I'M GOING TO FEEL WORSE BUT THAT'S NORMAL. IT MEANS MY BODY'S WORKING PROPERLY. DON'T FOCUS ON IT BEFORE IT'S EVEN COME!

PROBLEMS WITH FRIENDS AND FAMILY...

Seeing Mum and Dad arguing can be upsetting.

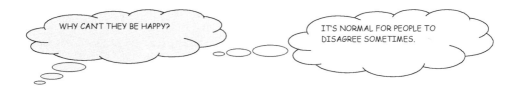

WHY CAN'T THEY BE HAPPY?

IT'S NORMAL FOR PEOPLE TO DISAGREE SOMETIMES.

You may feel your friends have moved on.

MY FRIENDS HAVE ALL MOVED ON AND LEFT ME BEHIND.

THERE'S NO REASON WHY I CAN'T CATCH UP WITH THINGS ONCE I'M BETTER!

PERFECTIONISM

What is it?

Perfectionism is a tendency to set very high, rigid standards for yourself, your performance or achievements or to feel displeased with anything that is not perfect or does not meet extremely high standards.

Perfectionism can help but can also be unhelpful, depending on the situation.

If you are a perfectionist you may not feel happy with your work until it is exceptional, and will be used to doing excellent pieces of work, or always achieving grade As. This is something to be proud of. It will have brought you praise and rewards.

However, being a perfectionist may leave you feeling miserable. You may spend so much of your time making things perfect that you have little time left for other activities or seeing friends. You may feel that you, or others, are never good enough and you may always be critical. You may feel nervous about everything you do because you think the result has to be perfect. You may not like trying new things because you're worried about making mistakes. You may be so worried about making things perfect that you don't get any enjoyment out of doing things.

CFS and Perfectionism

A recent study has found that adults with CFS were perfectionistic in an unhelpful way. They were worried about making mistakes and doubted their actions more. They were worried about being criticised and felt others expected them to be perfect. *If you set yourself high standards while you are ill and out of practice at doing things, you are bound to feel disappointed in yourself.*

Is perfection possible?

It's impossible to make something perfect! This is because **perfection doesn't exist.** Try this out – Find something that you think is perfect and then, look closer. Is it perfect in every single way? Eventually you will find something about it that could be better. If you try to achieve perfection in your life, you will always be disappointed.

It's important to recognise when perfectionism becomes unhelpful. Perfectionism becomes unhelpful when you spend a lot of time and energy over perfecting things which don't have to be perfect, or when you will not gain much out of making something perfect. If the tendency to want perfection is making you miserable, and wasting your time and energy, then here are some ways to overcome this tendency:

Ways to overcome perfectionism

☺ Ask yourself:

☺ *Is the time and effort you are spending improving something worth it to you and others?*
☺ *Would others be satisfied with what you've produced?*
☺ *Have you achieved what you were asked to?*
☺ *Do you really need to do more?*

For example if you have been asked to draw a diagram for your homework, aim to make it neat, clear and get the message across. As a perfectionist you might be worried about your handwriting, the size of your margin, the angle of your lines, the colours you have used, not making any crossings out or using Tippex. Worrying about these things will take up your time and energy but it is unlikely to help you understand the work better or to get you a better grade.

- ⏲ Focus on the *doing* rather than the end result. For example, at school, instead of focusing on getting grade As you could focus on making a good effort in learning. You could make sure you attend most of your classes, make an effort to understand and take part in the classes, study regularly and review your learning every few weeks.

- ⏲ Set *time limits* on your activities for a week or so, so that you do them and then move on, whether or not you've produced a perfect result.

- ⏲ If you find you're slowing down on a task trying to make it perfect, think about whether you, and others, would be more pleased with a number of good efforts rather than one masterpiece.

Why are you perfectionistic?

Perhaps when you try to finish a task you don't feel quite right. You feel you should continue. Don't! Tell yourself that the feeling of anxiety may be uncomfortable but it won't harm you. The feelings may rise but they will eventually peak and then trail off.

You might be perfectionistic because you worry about being criticised or making mistakes. If you're 'perfect', no one can disapprove of you or criticise you.

Ask yourself "What's the worst that could happen if I don't do this perfectly?" Check your answers for the thinking errors covered earlier, such as thinking in Black and White terms, Predicting the Future, Mind Reading, or being too hard on yourself.

If you do get disapproval or criticism for less than an A grade this is not a disaster. You are not a robot but a human being, and you can cope with less than perfect results. Everybody makes mistakes and we learn from them, so accept that you will make mistakes sometimes, rather than using up a lot of your energy trying not to.

If you don't expect yourself to do things perfectly, you will get more satisfaction out of what you do. You don't have to do things 100% perfectly to enjoy them. You will have more fun and maybe you will be more fun to be with!

Lower your standards and you will enjoy life more. Sometimes being average is much more fun!

STRESSFUL EVENTS

We all have to cope with stressful events from time to time. We may be faced with a demanding situation, or we may have to go through a change in our lives. For example, exam time, moving schools/college, moving house, relationship break-ups, or losing someone close to you are all stressful life events.

When we are stressed and our feelings are running high, we can start to think in unhelpful ways. As well as keeping a check on our thinking to make sure we are not making the mistakes covered earlier, it can be helpful to look at these challenges in a different way.

Looking at challenges in a different way

When we're faced with a problem or a challenge we can start to think in **'All or Nothing'** terms.

For example, Exam Time can be a challenge. If you look more closely you will see that your exams are actually just a series of separate tests in different subjects.

To help you see your exams in a different way, you could make a table like the one overleaf. List all the subjects in one column. You will like some subjects more than others and do better in some of the subjects than in others.

In the next column, write the grade you expect to get. Be realistic. If it's less than what you'd like it will 'ground' your worries and help you to face them. On the other hand, you might discover that things aren't as bad as they seemed! Then, when you get your results write the grade you actually got in the last column. You might find that you were expecting too much of yourself, or that you lived up to your expectations, or even that you were underestimating yourself.

Subject	Expected grade	Actual grade
maths	C	C
english	B	C
science	D	C
geography	B	A
R.E	C	D
french	C	B

Another way to help you think about your exam results is to draw an Exam Result Number Line for each subject, like the one below. Put a cross on the line showing what result you expect to get. Then write on your actual grade when you get it. Marking your results on a line will help you to not see them in All or Nothing terms.

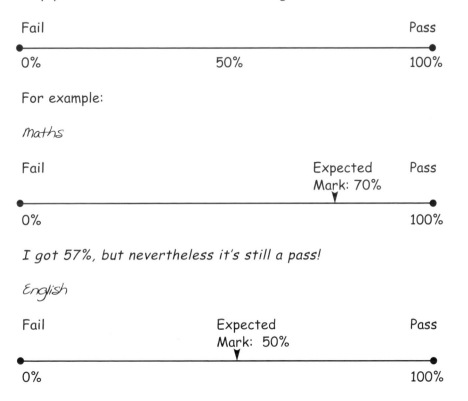

Fail   Pass

0%   50%   100%

For example:

Maths

Fail   Expected   Pass
                                          Mark: 70%

0%   100%

I got 57%, but nevertheless it's still a pass!

English

Fail   Expected   Pass
                              Mark: 50%

0%   100%

I got 68%. I'm really pleased!

These tricks help you to see your exams in a new light.

You can use these tricks with any challenge. *Whatever you're worried about, it helps to break up the challenge and look at the different parts of it.* Then you can tackle the small parts of the challenge one at a time.

DEALING WITH WORRIES

If you have been ill for a long time it is likely that your lifestyle has changed and you have stopped doing a lot of the things that you used to do. As you get better, although you may feel good about starting these activities again, you may have worries about them, for example, "Will I be able to cope?"

These worries are normal quite simply because if we don't do something regularly we lose confidence in our ability to do it.

COMMON WORRIES OF PEOPLE WITH CFS

Below are some of the worries that people with CFS often describe to us.

going back to school   catching up with missed work

coping with schoolwork   starting new studies

catching up with friends   playing sports

taking up activities again   becoming ill again

not knowing what to tell people at school/college
or friends about their illness

For some people these worries can be so severe that they can stop them from doing something they really want to do. The next section is about dealing with your worries.

HOW TO DEAL WITH YOUR WORRIES
– using PROBLEM SOLVING

Make a list of any situations or activities that worry you. Decide what you want to tackle first. It might be better to tackle the things that you are least worried about first. As you become more confident you can tackle the more worrying situations. The box below describes how to solve problems in steps.

PROBLEM SOLVING

1. What is your problem?

Write down clearly and exactly what your problem is.

2. Think of at least 3 different ways to solve the problem.

Try to see the problem from the point of view of someone who you think is good at solving problems or has dealt with similar problems in he past: " If _____ was in my shoes what would he/she do?"

3. Write down what you think the result of each of your solutions might be.

4. Decide which solution you think would give the best result.

5. Make a plan and carry out that solution.

6. Did your solution work?

Use the form on the next page to write down your problem solving. This way of solving problems may seem long and boring, but once you have done this a few times you may find that you can solve problems in your head without having to write them down. Make some time to tackle your worries in this way in your Activity Programme.

As well as certain problems, you may have feelings of anxiety which are making it harder for you to tackle your problems. This is discussed in the next section.

PROBLEM SOLVING SHEET

MY PROBLEM: ....

ALTERNATIVE SOLUTIONS:
(Think of at least 3.)

1. ....
....

2. ....
....

3. ....
....

4. ....
....

EVALUATE SOLUTIONS:
(What is a possible outcome
of each solution.)

1. ....
....

2. ....
....

3. ....
....

4. ....
....

THE BEST SOLUTION IS NO. ....

MY PLAN TO CARRY OUT THE SOLUTION:

....
....
....

EVALUATE YOUR PLAN:

Did you follow your plan?
....

Was the outcome as you expected?
....

Are you satisfied with the
result?...
Would you use the same solution
again?..

PROBLEM SOLVING SHEET

EXAMPLE

MY PROBLEM : *My course-work needs to be in by the end of the week and there's no way I"ll get it done.*

ALTERNATIVE SOLUTIONS:
(Think of at least 3.)

1. *I could just forget about. it and give up?*

2. *I could stay up all night and work really hard.*

3. *I could just hand it in late.*

4. *I could ask for an extension.*

EVALUATE SOLUTIONS:
(What is a possible result of ach solution.)

1. *I"ll feel down. I may have to start the subject over again.*

2. *I"ll be exhausted for ages. That might set me back with other work.*

3. *It might not be accepted.*

4. *They're very strict about that sort of thing. They might say no - that teacher doesn't have much sympathy.*

THE BEST SOLUTION IS NO.   4

MY PLAN TO CARRY OUT THE SOLUTION:
I."ll ask the teacher who knows most about my illness about the policy for extensions, and get them to speak to my teacher about it. They can then tell me what I have to do.

EVALUATE YOUR PLAN:

Did you follow your plan? *Yes*

Was the outcome as you expected? *Not quite - I needed a letter from the CFS clinic too - but I got that and I've got an extension!*

Are you satisfied with the result? *Yes, very much.*

Would you use the same solution again? *Yes and next time I'd know what to do.*

DEALING WITH ANXIETY

WHAT IS ANXIETY?

We all feel anxious from time to time. Anxiety can help us react to a stressful situation. It can help us to think and act quickly in situations like exams or interviews, or if we are in danger. **Feeling anxious is part of our normal behaviour.**

The symptoms of anxiety can be mild, when we just feel tense or 'wound up'. They can also be severe, when we experience feelings of dread, fear or panic.

You may find that you have uncomfortable feelings of anxiety when you have to do something new or something that you haven't done for a long time. You may be lacking confidence, or just be out of practice. The feelings of anxiety may be making it hard for you to do things you really want to.

Understanding how anxiety affects our body, our thoughts and our behaviour helps us to cope with it.

The Effects of Anxiety on our Body: Anxiety leads to many different symptoms in the body. These symptoms are mainly due to a rise of adrenalin in the blood. Common signs of extreme anxiety are shown below:

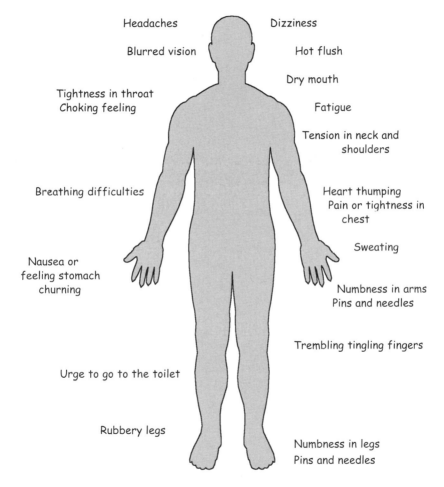

Headaches

Blurred vision

Dizziness

Hot flush

Dry mouth

Tightness in throat
Choking feeling

Fatigue

Tension in neck and
shoulders

Breathing difficulties

Heart thumping
Pain or tightness in
chest

Sweating

Nausea or
feeling stomach
churning

Numbness in arms
Pins and needles

Trembling tingling fingers

Urge to go to the toilet

Rubbery legs

Numbness in legs
Pins and needles

These physical symptoms can be very uncomfortable and distressing. It is easy to think that there is something seriously wrong, but it is important to remember that they cannot harm you. **They are the body's normal reaction to stress.**

The Effects of Anxiety on our Behaviour: Anxiety affects what we do. It can lead us to avoid situations which make us feel anxious.

The Effects of Anxiety on our Thoughts: Anxiety can make worrying thoughts race through our minds making it hard to concentrate.

THE VICIOUS CIRCLE OF ANXIETY

The different effects of anxiety on our body, thoughts and behaviour are *linked* and can *fuel each other* so that we become caught in a vicious circle of anxiety that is hard to break out of.

> **Body:**
> We experience a variety of distressing bodily symptoms, for example, headaches, dizziness, fatigue, blurred vision.

> **Thoughts:**
> We tend to worry and have unhelpful thoughts, such as "I can't cope" and "I'm not ready for this". We may think there is something seriously wrong as we experience bodily symptoms of anxiety.

> **Behaviour:**
> We may avoid certain situations because they make us feel anxious. This can make us even more anxious when we have to face the situation again, as we are not used to dealing with it.

HOW TO COPE WITH ANXIETY

This section tells you how to cope with anxiety which has led you to avoiding certain situations, such as seeing friends.

Therapists have found that Exposure Therapy is a good way of helping people with anxiety. Exposure therapy involves facing the situations that make you feel anxious, until you feel less anxious. This is possible because anxiety comes down by itself with time.

The more often you do the thing that makes you feel anxious, and the longer you do that thing, the quicker you will get used to it and the less it will make you feel anxious. If you only face the situation that makes you anxious occasionally it's likely that you will feel anxious every time you face that situation.

Your therapist will help you carry out some exposure therapy if it is appropriate for you.

Here are some hints to make Exposure Therapy effective:

☺ **BE CLEAR ABOUT WHAT YOU ARE GOING TO DO**
eg. phone a friend for 15 minutes

☺ **STAY IN THE SITUATION UNTIL YOU FEEL BETTER**
Feeling anxious is not pleasant but it cannot harm you!
Wait, and let your feelings of anxiety pass.

☺ **FACE THE SITUATION AS OFTEN AS YOU CAN**
eg. phone a friend once a day

☺ **EXPECT YOURSELF TO FEEL ANXIOUS**

☺ **KEEP A DIARY OF YOUR EXPOSURE TASKS**
This will help you to see how much you have achieved. *(See Chart G)*

THE
FUTURE

MAINTAINING GAINS AFTER TREATMENT

Keeping up Improvements

To keep up the improvements you have made, such as the activities you practice, **make them part of your everyday life.**

- Make sure your days are balanced between activity and rest, and don't fall back into the trap of the 'boom and bust' cycle by doing too much some days and too little on others.
- Keep up your regular sleep routine.
- Take 30 minutes of exercise 2-3 times every week. This will keep you fit.
- Keep your expectations of yourself at a manageable level, and feel good about what you achieve.

Building on Improvements

You can work on problems by yourself. *Take things gradually.* Set yourself weekly targets, broken down into manageable chunks. Once you can do them without feeling too tired, keep them part of your normal routine.

Watch out for unhelpful thoughts. For example, you might find yourself thinking that you can't do it. Feeling afraid is normal but it does not mean you are going to fail. Keep diaries of these unhelpful thoughts and the more helpful ones too. Remember that you've made a lot of progress to come this far and there is no reason why you shouldn't be able to take the final steps to recovery.

POTENTIAL FUTURE PROBLEMS

Once you've improved there will be times when setbacks may occur and it will help to be prepared for them. **They are likely to happen at difficult times,** for example, during an infection, during exam time at school, or if you have an argument with a friend.

During an Infection
If you have an infection your CFS symptoms may get worse. You should expect this. If you have taken your temperature with a thermometer and find your temperature is high, then you should rest for a while. If you are feeling weak but don't have a temperature you should cut out your sporting activities. If you have a cold you should try to carry on as usual.

Exam Time
We've found in our experience that exams can be a difficult time for people with CFS. That's why we've included a separate section on coping with exams. Read this at least six weeks before your exams start.

Difficulties with Friends
Disagreements or arguments with friends can be upsetting. Everybody has problems like these from time to time. They are normal and help you learn about relationships. If you find yourself worrying a lot, write down your worries. Then, write down a different way of looking at the situation. It can be helpful to talk to your Mum or Dad or another family member or friend about them.

WAYS TO HELP YOU STUDY

Make it easy to start!

Keep your work place a nice place
Keep a particular place for working and make this place attractive to you. Get rid of unnecessary things and leave it tidy after each study session.

Make a list of what you want to do
Write a list of the things you're going to work on and the order you're going to do them. Make sure you'll be able to manage them in the time available.

Keep in mind why you're studying
Write down the things you will gain from studying and read the list when you need a boost or when you feel discouraged.

Planning – use the Salami Principle!

Whether you've got a big project, a lot of catching up, or revision to do, a good way to plan your work is the salami principle: if you eat the slices one by one you will eventually eat the whole salami. So, cut big projects into slices! **So set yourself small tasks and you'll eventually complete the large task!**

The Study Period

Use the Chocolate Box approach:
Give yourself small chunks to study, with lots of variety, just like a box of chocolates! You'll find it easier to work your way through the work this way.

Make each study period about 35 minutes long. This is how long most people can concentrate well. Spend the first 20 minutes learning new stuff, then have a few minutes break. Spend the next few minutes revising what you learned yesterday, a week ago and a month ago. Then spend the last 5 minutes revising what you've just learned that day. This will help to stop you forgetting what you have learned.

Reward yourself for each study period
You will enjoy studying more if it's rewarding. Keep the rewards simple and have them soon after your study session.

STUDY SKILLS

Reading

When reading for studying use the 4-pronged approach:

Prepare – Before starting to read, think about what you already know about the subject.

Overview - Read the index, headings and summary. You'll be learning about the organisation and content of the text.

Closer reading - Read the parts you need to read.

Review - review what you've read and learned.

This approach will help you remember what you've read and won't waste time!

Making Notes

Before you make notes ask yourself how you will use them. Do they need to be detailed so that you don't have to look at the book again, or short notes to remind you of the main points? They should suit **your** needs and include only what **you** need to know.
Do something with the information you've learned: draw a colourful diagram, explain it to someone else, or make tapes of the information - make it fun!

COPING WITH EXAMS

Long-term Planning

<u>Ask yourself</u>:

What is it essential to know? Which topics do you know, and where are the gaps in your knowledge?

Make a plan of what to study when, and write it down. Plan to revise everything a second time but in a 1/4 of the time it first took you. Include some 'Extra Time' for topics that are difficult, and in case you fall behind (this happens to most people).

Remember it's never possible to know *everything.*

Daily Strategy

- ⏱ Study one topic at a time for a set amount of time, and stop when the time is up and move onto the next one. That way you don't concentrate on one topic and miss out on the others. If you have exam questions from previous years, practice answering them. This will make the exam less daunting.
- ⏱ Make sure you have short breaks throughout the day, and take a whole day off each week.
- ⏱ Don't stay up all night revising or drink too much coffee as this may upset your sleep pattern. It's important to eat, sleep, and exercise regularly as this will keep you feeling fit and healthy.

Exam Day

- ☺ Look at the notes you've been working from, not at new material as this may confuse you.
- ☺ Don't listen to scare mongering from others as this will make you stressed unnecessarily. Worrying at this point will not change anything.

- ☺ When the exam begins read the instructions and questions carefully, and plan your time.
- ☺ If you get stuck in the middle of the exam, start to write notes - this will trigger your memory.
- ☺ Don't feel you have to write down everything you know and don't feel you have to be a genius -just answer the questions you are asked.

Exam Nerves

It's normal to worry before an exam, so don't worry about being very worried! Instead think of yourself as feeling more alert. If you find yourself thinking of all the things that could go wrong, ignore these thoughts - they're a sign of anxiety and you don't have to believe them!

Remember that your exam result will only reflect how you did in that particular exam in that subject. Even if you fail, ask yourself: "Will it matter in 100 years' time? Or even, who will remember in 2 years' time?" This will help you keep the failure in perspective, and see it as a temporary setback, not a judgement of you as a person.

GOOD LUCK!

A FINAL NOTE

Making the changes described in this book is not easy. They take a lot of hard work, time, and courage. There will be times when it doesn't go well but it's the overall picture you need to focus on. If you have a setback for whatever reason don't be too hard on yourself. No one can do things perfectly all the time.

Good Luck!

USEFUL CHARTS TO HELP YOU

CHART A

Fill in this diary every morning.
Guess the time it takes you to fall asleep, and how long you are awake for during the night.

	example	Mon	Tues	Wed	Thurs	Fri	Sat	Sun
1. I went to bed at ... o'clock and turned the lights out at ... o'clock.	10.30 11.15							
2. After turning the lights out I fell asleep in ... minutes.	60 min							
3. My sleep was interrupted ... times (write the number of times you remember waking during the night)	2 20							
4. My sleep was interrupted for ... minutes (write how long you were awake for each time)	40							
5. I woke up at ... o'clock (the last time you woke up)	7.15							
6. I got out of bed for the day at ... o'clock.	8.10							
7. Overall, my sleep was ... (0 = very sound, 8 = very restless)	6							
8. When I got up this morning I felt ... (0 = refreshed, 8 = exhausted)	7							
9. In total I slept ... hours.	6 hours							

NO. OF HOURS SLEEP LAST NIGHT	MONDAY	TUESDAY	WEDNESDAY	THURSDAY	FRIDAY	SATURDAY	SUNDAY
8 – 10							
10 -11							
11 – 12							
12 – 1							
1 – 2							
2 – 3							
3 -4							
4 – 5							
5 -6							
6 – 7							
7 -8							
8 -12mn							
TIME I WENT TO SLEEP							

CHART C

GOAL BREAKDOWN SHEET

1) Goal:

....

Targets:

....
....
....
....

2) Goal:

....

Targets:

....
....
....
....

3) Goal:

....

Targets:

....
....
....
....

Self Help For Chronic Fatigue Syndrome

	MONDAY	TUESDAY	WEDNESDAY	THURSDAY	FRIDAY	SATURDAY	SUNDAY
7-8							
8-9							
9-10							
10-11							
11-12							
12-1							
1-2							
2-3							
3-4							
4-5							
5-6							
6-7							
7-8							
8-9							
9-10							
10-11							

CHART E

PATHWAYS TOWARDS CHANGE

DATE:

1.

	DATES						

SELF-RATING SCALE: 3=FULLY DONE 2=DONE QUITE A LOT 1=DONE A LITTLE 0=NOT DONE

YOU MAY LIKE TO ADD NOTES ON THE BACK OF THIS SHEET.

Self Help For Chronic Fatigue Syndrome

Date	Situation What were you doing/thinking?	Unhelpful Thoughts Rate belief (0 – 100%)	Alternative Response Rate belief in each one (0-100%)

EXPOSURE TASK RECORD

Record your activities and rate how anxious you feel before, during and after each Exposure task, using the scale below.

| 0 | 1 | 2 | 3 | 4 | 5 | 6 | 7 | 8 |

No anxiety/   Slight   Moderate   Marked   Severe anxiety/ distress

Date	Time start/finish	Task	Before	During	After	Comments